THEY MUST BE JOKING

B & C Publications

They Must Be Joking

B&C Publications
5 College Street
Stratford-upon-Avon
Warwickshire
CV37 6BN

www.claireika.co.uk

Printed and bound in Great Britain

ISBN: 978-1-78280-191-7

THEY MUST BE JOKING

A light-hearted look at some serious research

Beryl Downing

with illustrations by
Claire Reika Wright

CONTENTS

Author's Note

This is a collection of contradictions and rum research. Yesterday eggs were bad for us, tomorrow they won't hurt at all. Last week jogging until we are breathless would help us live longer; today too much exercise could damage our heart and knees. And what's all the fuss about red wine being good for you? According to some scientific research it could actually cause cancer.

A lot of apparently pointless probing could turn out to be valuable because it may lead to greater things. But some conclusions are so obvious they don't warrant expensively trained scientists having a mental holiday while they prove that 'The more you drink the more attractive you think you are' (page 150).

Also, it's worth remembering that publicity fuels credibility and it is in the interests of the researchers to be published in the main stream press as well as in medical journals – and as health is a major obsession these days, the dottier the conclusion, the bigger the headline.

The one bit of advice no one has yet tested scientifically is to take everything with a pinch of salt. Just be careful it doesn't clog up your arteries.

HEALTH

When does a good intention become an obsession? When it creates more stress than it cures. We are bombarded with information on how to live longer, but if the Worried Well stopped popping pills 'just in case', they might find more time to enjoy the life they've got.

Calm Down Dear!.......

Competitive and aggressive people are twice as likely as their calmer colleagues to suffer a stroke. Impatient personalities were found to be as much at risk of a stroke as people who smoked.

Sample: 150 stroke patients, 300 healthy ones. Average age 54. San Carlos University Hospital, Madrid. August 2012.

…….. or Stamp and Shout

On the other hand, you could die from a stiff upper lip. Those who internalised their problems were found to suffer from a raised pulse, resulting in high blood pressure.

Sample: 6,000 adults. University of Jena. December 2012.

Doctors of Literature?

Try reading before reaching for a prescription. A list of 27 books has been drawn up for doctors to recommend to depressed patients before agreeing to drug treatment. Apart from self-help feel-good books, the list includes several modern authors from Nancy Mitford to Salman Rushdie. *Department of Health. February 2013.*

A Clean Sweep

Women can reduce the risk of breast cancer by doing two-and-a-half hours of housework a day. Six hours is even better but if polishing doesn't appeal walking or gardening will do. *Sample: 8,034 cancer cases over 11 years from 257,805 participants in the European Prospective Investigation of Cancer, funded by Cancer Research UK. September 2012.*

But don't kid yourself. Women who count housework or gardening as exercise are fatter than those who don't – possibly because they overestimate how much effort they have put in and give themselves a calorific treat as a reward. *Sample: 4,500 men and women. University of Ulster. October 2013.*

Snoring Warning

Cure the snoring to stay healthy. Snoring could increase the risk of cancer by up to five times, as low oxygen levels caused by sleep-disordered breathing could stimulate tumours. *Sample: 1,500 adults for 22 years. University of Wisconsin-Madison. May 2012.*

Bone of Contention

Calcium tablets taken to strengthen thinning bones could instead give you a heart attack. People who took calcium on its own had double the risk of a heart attack than those who avoided it or took it with other supplements. You could do better just eating more calcium-rich foods like milk, cheese and green vegetables. *Sample: 24,000 adults tracked for 11 years. University of Auckland. May 2012.*

Pills are a Headache

Taking aspirin, ibuprofen or paracetamol for more than 10 to 15 days can cause headaches, rather than curing them. The brain becomes more sensitive to pain which results in more headaches. *NICE, the health watchdog. September 2012.*

....But a low dose could help breast cancer patients by reducing the rate of tumour growth and boosting the effect of tamoxifen, widely used to treat the disease. *Sample: Mice. University of Kansas. April 2013.*

Wait and See

Taking one 100mg tablet of aspirin every other day could cut the risk of bowel and stomach cancer, but you may have to wait a while for proof. After ten years there was no difference in the number of women developing cancer, but after 18 years the risk was lower.
Sample: Nearly 15,000 women over 45. Harvard University and Brigham and Women's Hospital, Boston. November 2012.

P-p-p-Pick up a Paintbrush

Painting and drawing improves self-esteem. Researchers found that 88 per cent of people with anxiety and depression problems said they were more confident and more motivated after taking part in an art course. Their relationships with other people improved, too. *Anglia Ruskin/ South East Partnership University NHS Trust. October 2012.*

Cheer Up Sunshine!

Low levels of vitamin D, which comes from sunlight on the skin and eating oily fish, can make children more likely to suffer from depression. Those with the highest levels have a ten per cent lower risk of developing the problem.

Sample: 2,700 children. Bristol University. January 2012.

Going Up in Smoke

Even one cigarette a day could accelerate a heart attack. Women who smoked one to 14 cigarettes a day faced nearly twice the risk of death from heart attack than non-smokers. But the risk could be reduced in five years if they stopped smoking while they were still healthy.

Sample: 101,000 women. University of Alberta. December 2012.

A Song in Your Heart

Join a choir to improve your health. Singing helps to synchronise your heart beats, which reduces the risk of cardiac disease. It's as good for you as yoga. *Gothenburg University, Sweden. July 2013.*

Sitting Targets

Middle-aged men who sit at their desks for more than four hours are more likely to report illnesses such as cancer, diabetes and heart disease. Researchers were not sure whether the sitting time led to diseases, or whether the diseases influenced the sitting time. *Sample: 63,048 men aged 45 to 65. Kansas State University. February 2013.*

Get Up and Go

However, you can lower your blood sugar and insulin levels and fend off diabetes by taking a short, brisk stroll round the desks in the office. Workers who wandered about every half hour were less likely to develop type 2 diabetes than those who didn't budge. *University of Otago. July 2013.*

Do-Gooding

Voluntary workers who put in at least four hours of unpaid help a week decreased their risk of high blood pressure by 40 per cent. The type of voluntary work didn't matter - the social connection was what helped. *Sample: 1,164 adults aged 51 to 91. Carnegie Mellon University. June 2013.*

Rosehips All the Way

Blood pressure and cholesterol levels drop when you have a daily dose of rose hips. Obese patients who took a capsule or a solution made from 40 grams of powder reduced their risk of developing type 2 diabetes and heart disease. The hips are full of vitamin C. *Sample: 61 men and women for 12 weeks. Lund University, Sweden. January 2012.*

Gumming Up the Works

Brush your teeth to avoid dementia. An 18 year study showed that people who didn't brush their teeth every day were up to 65 per cent more likely to develop memory loss, perhaps because gum disease bacteria can cause inflammation and brain damage.

Sample: 5,000 elderly adults. University of California. August 2012.

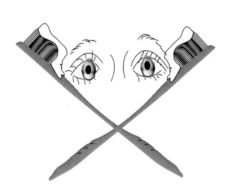

Rosemary for remembrance

Sniffing rosemary could not only improve your mood, but help your brain power. The higher level of the oil people took into the blood, the better their speed and accuracy. *Northumbria University. February 2012.*

Sunny Outlook?

Tanning under a sunbed could raise the risk of several slow-growing skin cancers in addition to serious melanoma. Those tanning indoors could increase the risk significantly if they are under 25. *Sample: 9,328 non-melanoma cases. University of California, San Francisco. October 2012.*

......**On the other hand**, sitting in the sun for a short time reduces blood pressure. Volunteers spent two sessions of 20 minutes each under a tanning lamp. In one session they were exposed to heat only. In the other they were treated with heat plus ultraviolet rays found in sunlight. Their blood pressure went down under the UV rays and, as strokes and heart attacks cause many times more deaths than skin cancer, the benefit of sitting in the sun for short periods was thought to outweigh the risks. *Sample: 24 adults. Edinburgh University. May 2013.*

Ginkgo No-no

Taking ginkgo biloba to prevent memory loss could be a waste of time. Four per cent of people given 120 mg of the extract twice a day for five years were diagnosed with probable Alzheimer's, compared with five percent of those give a placebo. *Sample: 2,820 over-70s. Hôpital Casselardit, Toulouse. September 2012.*

Perils of Country Life

People brought up in rural areas could be twice as likely to suffer from Alzheimer's in old age, but it could be because city dwellers had easier access to health care. *Sample:12,580 people in several countries. Edinburgh University. September 2012.*

Zzzzzzzzzz

A good night's sleep is the best medicine. While we are sleeping the brain is busy removing toxins which could lead to Alzheimer's and other neurological diseases. If it happened when we are awake we wouldn't be able to think as clearly because the process takes up a lot of energy getting rid of the chemical rubbish which builds up during waking hours. *Sample: mice. University of Rochester Medical Centre, New York. October 2013.*

FOOD

If your diet doesn't get you, the Food Police will. Small quantities of the dreaded butter, salt and sugar all make food taste better and there are plenty of studies to prove that substitutes and supplements are no better for you. The Balanced Diet theory never did anyone any harm.

EGGS-PERT OPINIONS

Two eggs a day won't hurt. Heart disease patients had no negative impact on their cholesterol and blood pressure after eating them – or half a cup of egg substitute – daily for six weeks. *Yale University. April 2013.*

Even three a day is good for you. After 12 weeks good cholesterol improved and subjects who otherwise ate a carbohydrate-restricted diet were better able to remove cholesterol from the blood. *University of Connecticut. April 2013.*

Contrariwise, some scientists found that lecithin, found in egg yolks, can increase the risk of heart disease.
Cleveland Clinic Lerner Research Institute. April 2013.

But one egg a day does no harm to healthy people. Three earlier studies showed that eggs contain nutrients which could help lower the risk of heart disease, despite containing a lot of cholesterol.
Harvard School of Public Health, 1999, 2006 and 2008.

They Must Be Joking

FAT CHANCE

Milky Way

Milk, yogurt, cheese and even ice cream can boost the memory as well as build healthy bones. People who ate dairy products five or six times a week did better in memory tests than those who rarely touched them. *Sample: 972 men and women aged 23 to 98. University of Maine. January 2012.*

....but

One portion of yogurt or ice cream could hinder recovery from breast cancer because full-fat products contain oestrogen which can encourage the growth of tumours. *Sample: 1,500 women cancer patients. Kaiser Permanent Research Centre, California. March 2013.*

...and yet

If you eat about 60g (half a small pot) of yogurt a day you are less likely to develop high blood pressure. The calcium keeps blood vessels more supple. Taking calcium in pill form, though, could have the opposite effect. *Sample: 2,000 adults. University of Minnesota. September 2012.*

Say Cheese

Cheese or yogurt can help you to stay healthy. Eating 55g a day reduces the risk of type 2 diabetes by 12 per cent. The 'probiotic' bacteria in both foods lowers cholesterol and produces certain vitamins which prevent diabetes. *Sample: 16,800 healthy adults and 12,400 patients with diabetes from 8 European countries. American Journal of Clinical Nutrition. July 2012.*

Moreover, Roquefort cheese could be the answer to the curious fact that French people enjoy good health despite eating a diet high in saturated fat. The mould and blue-green veins in the cheese could guard against inflammation caused by arthritis and cardiovascular disease.
Lycotec, Cambridge. December 2012.

Also, cutting out fatty foods alters the brain chemistry and makes you depressed because it can start a cycle of poor eating. *University of Montreal. December 2012.*

FEELING FRUITY

Keeping the Doctor Away

An apple a day for four weeks lowered the 'bad' cholesterol of healthy, middle-aged men and women by 40 per cent. *Ohio State University. October 2012. (Research funded by an apple industry group).*

Berry, Berry

Eating strawberries, blueberries and other summer fruits every other day cuts the risk of heart attacks by up to a third. The flavonoids in berries are the same as those in tea and red wine. *Sample: 93,600 women for 18 years. Harvard School of Public Health, Boston. January 2013.*

A Hardening Attitude?

European watchdogs banned producers from claiming that prunes have a laxative effect. There was 'insufficient evidence,' they said, of a link between eating prunes and achieving a normal 'function.'

European Food Safety Authority. December 2011.

Skin Deep

Eating a couple of extra portions of fruit and veg a day makes you more attractive. Too many carrots turns the skin orange, but even a small amount of extra tomatoes, red and green peppers, broccoli and spinach give you a healthy glow and apples, blueberries and cherries cause an attractive flush. *Sample: 35 adults for six weeks. St Andrews University. March 2012.*

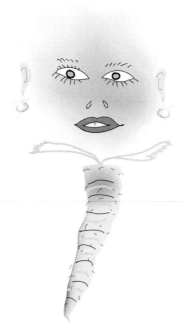

CHOCOLATE

High Jinks

Chocolate affects the brain in the same way as opium, which is what makes it hard to resist – addictive even. Eating chocolate results in a surge of a brain chemical which produces pleasurable feelings.

Sample: rats. University of Michigan. September 2012.

Raise the Bar

Men who eat a bar of chocolate a week are less likely to have a stroke. Those who ate 2.2oz (63g) of chocolate – milk as well as plain – had a 17 per cent lower risk of stroke. *Sample: 37,103 men aged 49 to 75 for 10 years. Karolinska Institutet, Stockholm. August 2012.*

FISHY STORIES

Oiling the Wheels

Eating oily fish could help you live longer. Older people with high levels of Omega-3 fatty acids, found in salmon, sardines and mackerel, cut their risk of dying from heart disease by more than a third. *Sample: 2,700 over-65s for 16 years. Harvard School of Public Health and the University of Washington. April 2013.*

Stop Taking the Tablets:

Oily fish eaten up to four times a week will make you six per cent less likely to have a stroke. But it has to be eaten, not taken as a supplement. *Sample 800,000 people from 15 countries. Cambridge University and others. October 2012.*

On the other hand, Omega-3 in tablet form could help if you eat a lot of junk food. Fish oils could counteract the refined sugars and saturated fats which can stop protective hormones passing into the brain. *University of Liverpool. May 2013.*

Jack Sprat

Fish oil is better for women than for men. It quadruples the effect on muscle cells that control the elasticity of blood vessels in women and only doubles the effect in men. *Sample: 30 men and 30 women. University of Reading. October 2012.*

Change of Heart?

In 2007 the National Institute for Health and Clinical Excellence (NICE) advised people to eat two or three portions of oily fish each week and approved fish oil supplements on the NHS. Six years later it now says that new treatments for heart attacks or strokes means an oily fish diet might be of minimal benefit. *NICE. June 2013.*

Fruit and Nut Cases

The Mediterranean diet of fruit, nuts, vegetables, whole grains, fish, white meat and olive oil is better at cutting the risk of heart attacks than just a low-fat diet. *University of Barcelona. February 2013.*

No-Brainer

.....**And it** helps your head as well as your heart by protecting against the development of lesions linked to memory problems. *Sample: 1,000 over-70s. University of Miami Miller School of Medicine. February 2012.*

Mood Food

.....**What's more,** it can also reduce the risk of depression by nearly a third. *University of Las Palmas de Gran Canaria and University Clinic of Navarra. December 2012.*

A Cracking Idea

Seven a day is what you need when it comes to walnuts. They contain high levels of polyphenol, which can protect from tissue damage and lower cholesterol.
University of Scranton, Pennsylvania. January 2012.

Calories – what calories?

Nuts don't put on weight, so people who avoid eating them because they contain lots of calories, needn't limit their consumption after all. In a review of 31 studies, people who added nuts to their diet or replaced other foods with nuts actually lost slightly more weight than those who didn't. In addition, almonds, hazels, Brazils, walnuts, cashews and peanuts help reduce the risk of heart disease.   *American Journal of Clinical Nutrition. October 2013.*

Nuts to Diabetes.....

A 26g packet of walnuts per week can reduce the risk of type 2 diabetes by almost a quarter. *Sample: 140,000 women. Harvard School of Public Health, Boston. April 2013 .*

....and to Heart Disease

Just four hours after eating a handful of shelled walnuts (85g) cholesterol levels and blood vessel flexibility improves considerably, which long term could protect against heart disease. *Sample: 15 adults with high cholesterol. Penn State University, Pennsylvania. May 2013.*

Curry Cure

The turmeric in curry could help to fight disease by killing a broad range of bacteria. The spice contains Curcumin which increases a protein that helps the immune system. You may have to eat a lot of curry to benefit. *Oregon State University. May 2012.*

Do Hold Your Breath

Raw garlic eaten twice a week reduces the risk of lung cancer by 44 per cent. Even smokers had a 30 per cent reduction. Researchers did not record whether it reduced friendships by the same amount. *Sample: 6,724 adults. Jiangsu Provincial Centre for Disease Control and Prevention, China. August 2013.*

Steak Your Claim

Eat more steak, liver, spinach and nuts if you want to cut the risk of Alzheimer's. People with anaemia are more likely to develop the disease and these iron-rich foods will help to boost the blood count. *Sample: more than 2,500 adults aged 70 to 79. University of California, San Francisco. August 2013.*

......But guess what? Eat less red meat – it could increase levels of iron in the brain and contribute to the risk of Alzheimer's. *Sample: 31 Alzheimer's patients. University of California, Los Angeles. August 2013.*

It Takes All Sorts

Large amounts of liquorice eaten in pregnancy could make a child anxious and depressed in later life. Liquorice deactivates a barrier in the womb that protects the baby from high levels of hormones that build up in a mother's blood when she is stressed. *Weizmann Institute of Science, Israel. July 2013.*

DRINK

Moderation never grabbed a headline as newspapers are more interested in news worthiness than worthy research. So next time you fill your glass, whether it is wine or water, drink it with a good dose of scepticism.

Mother of All Contradictions

A baby's development is not harmed if the mother drinks a glass of wine every day during pregnancy. They even grow up to have better balance – a sign of good brain development in the womb – than children of non-drinkers. *Sample: 7,000 children. Bristol University. June 2013.*

.....but a child's attention span will be lower by the time it is five years old if a mother has nine or more drinks a week during pregnancy. However, the odd **binge won't hurt.** *Sample: 1,628 mothers, average age 31. Aarhus University Hospital, Denmark. June 2012.*

A child's growth can be stunted up to the age of five if expectant mums drink a large glass of wine a day. *Sample: 85 drinkers compared with 63 non drinkers. Harvard Medical School. August 2012.*

A baby's intelligence can be lowered by up to four IQ points if mothers drink one glass of wine a day during pregnancy. It depends on four genes which influence how quickly alcohol is broken down. *Sample: 4,167 mothers and children. Bristol and Oxford Universities. November 2012.*

Miracle Worker

The 'miracle' ingredient Resveratrol, found in red wine, could:

Cut the risk of bowel cancer if given as a medicinal dose equivalent to two glasses of wine. *Sample: Mice. Leicester University. December 2012.*

Improve balance in old people and prevent falls. But you may have to drink so much that you'd fall over anyway. *Sample: Mice. Duquesne University, Pittsburgh. August 2012.*

Cancel out the benefits of exercise if taken in pill form. Exercise lowers blood pressure and 'bad' cholesterol on its own. *Sample: 27 inactive men, aged around 65 for eight weeks. University of Copenhagen. July 2013.*

Protect the brain from depression and lower the risk of coronary heart disease in middle-aged and older people. *Sample: 5,500 light to moderate drinkers aged 55 to 80. University of Navarra, Spain. August 2013.*

But…..drinking red wine doesn't necessarily do you good. It contains very small amounts of resveratrol and even in moderate amounts alcohol increases the risk of several cancers. *Source: Cancer Research UK. October 2013.*

Bone up on This

One or two glasses of wine a day are as good as drugs for brittle bones. Regular moderate intake of alcohol after the menopause helps to keep bones strong. Abstinence leads to higher risk of osteoporosis. *University of Oregon. July 2012.*

Women who drink at least three 150ml glasses of wine or a pint of beer or two measures of spirits a week are 52 per cent less at risk from arthritis because of the effects of small amounts of alcohol on inflammation. *Sample: 34,100 women aged 39 to 84. Karolinska Institutet Stockholm. July 2012.*

They Must Be Joking

Creative Juices

Being too sober and too focused can blind you to novel possibilities. Twenty young men who were given four units of alcohol (two pints of beer or two medium glasses of wine) solved nearly 40 per cent more problems in 12 seconds per question than twenty sober ones who took an average of 15.5 seconds. *University of Illinois. April 2012.*

Mine's a Large Antioxidant.

It isn't the alcohol but the antioxidant compounds in red wine that are good for your heart. Men with a high risk of heart disease lowered their blood pressure after drinking non-alcoholic red wine every day for four weeks.
Sample: 67 men. University of Barcelona. September 2012.

Mixed Message

Drinking diet mixers to keep the weight down? You will be more drunk, but you won't feel it. Subjects given vodka became drunk more quickly with diet mixers than with sugary ones, but still thought they could drive, although they were over the drink-drive limit. *Sample: 16 men and women. Northern Kentucky University. February 2013.*

SOFT OPTIONS

Beet That!

Lower your blood pressure by seven per cent by drinking one 8oz cup of beetroot juice a day. The nitrate helps to increase oxygen in the body. *Sample: Eight women and seven men. Barts and the London School of Medicine. April 2013.*

Ward off dementia, too. Concentrated beetroot juice increases blood flow to the brain. *University of North Carolina. November 2010.*

Boost your stamina. Beetroot juice increased the staying power of healthy young men by up to 16 per cent. *University of Exeter. November 2010.*

Run faster, too. The nitrates relax the blood vessels, helping them work more efficiently. *St Louis University. April 2012.*

Getting the PR Juices Flowing

Heart disease? Stress? Pomegranate juice could be the answer, if you believe the manufacturers. People who took a capsule containing extract of the whole fruit, including pith, peel and seeds every day for a month, showed a decreased likelihood of cell damage which could affect brain, muscle, liver and kidney function. *Sample: 60 adults for one month. University of Murcia, funded by Pomegranate Pure-Plus. November 2011.*

......**But** at least independent research found that pomegranate juice is a natural aphrodisiac. Drinking it every day for a fortnight helped to raise testosterone levels 'significantly.' *Sample: 58 adults aged 21 to 64 for two weeks. Queen Margaret University, Edinburgh. December 2012.*

A Teething Problem

Don't give your children lots of juices and smoothies, thinking they are part of their five a day. You could be damaging their teeth. The acid erodes the tooth enamel and the natural sugars cause decay.
Royal College of Surgeons Dental Faculty.   March 2012

They Would Say That, Wouldn't They?

Eight glasses of water a day? That's what the bottled water industry insists we need. But nutrition and kidney specialists say this is an urban myth based on research first published in 1945, which did make the eight-a-day recommendation but went on to say that you can get a lot of this requirement from ordinary foods and other liquids. *Dartmouth Medical School, New Hampshire. June 2012.*

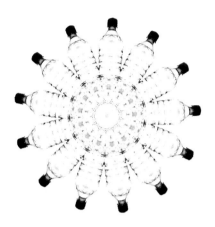

........**Moreover**, a different study found that water in food and beverages like tea and coffee contribute to the body's fluid requirements and there was no need to go round carrying a plastic water bottle like a fashion accessory. *La Trobe University, Melbourne. June 2012.*

COFFEE AND TEA

I Love Coffee, I Love Tea

One cup of coffee and two cups of green tea a day could lower the risk of stroke or heart by up to 20 per cent. But you mustn't drink too much coffee as it raises blood pressure. *Sample: 84,000 adults, 45 to 74, for 13 years. National Cerebral and Cardiovascular Center, Osaka. March 2013.*

Fatte Lattes

Too many lattes a day could cause serious heart problems, but one or two 'short' lattes could be good for you because habitual coffee drinking was associated with a lower risk of type 2 diabetes. *Sample: Five studies published between 2001 and 2011. Beth Israel Deaconess Medical Center, Boston. June 2012.*

A Dim View?

Scandinavians drink the most coffee and also have one of the highest rates of exfoliation glaucoma. Conclusion? Three cups of coffee a day could increase the risk of loss of vision. *Sample: 120,000 adults over 40 for 28 years. Brigham and Women's Hospital, Boston, US. October 2012.*

But a Bright Outlook?

But the French have found that that those who drink the most coffee and tea have the lowest blood pressure because the drinks contain health-giving flavonoids. *Preventive and Clinical Investigations Centre, Paris. July 2013.*

Pot Boilers

One to three cups of tea a day can cut the chance of memory loss by 43 per cent, particularly in women. Four cups help by 75 per cent. Tea contains theanine which protects against poisons that damage the brain. *Sample: 1,500 men and women in Singapore and 4,000 Americans for eight years. University of California. February 2013.*

Four cups of tea a day will also reduce the risk of a stroke by more than a fifth. **Less than that won't help.** *Sample: 74,961 adults for ten years. Karolinska Institutet, Stockholm. January 2013.*

Four cups of black tea a day could help reduce the risk of ovarian cancer. It's those flavonoids again. *Sample: 1,000 women, average age 50. Curtin University, Australia. November 2012.*

Five cups of green tea will help mobility. Pensioners who drank at least five cups a day were 33 per cent less likely to develop a disability than those who drank just one cup. But anyone on warfarin should avoid it. *Sample: 14,000 men and women aged 65 plus, for three years. Tokyo University. February 2012.*

Even a capsule of green tea, mixed with essence of pomegranate, turmeric and broccoli, can help lower the likelihood of prostate cancer by 63 per cent. *Bedford Hospital and Addenbrooke's Hospital, Cambridge. June 2013.*

I Should Co-Coa

Hot chocolate could stave off dementia. Two cups a day are enough to help pensioners' memories because chocolate boosts blood circulation, which the brain needs to function well. After drinking two cups a day for a month – but not consuming any other chocolate – pensioners improved their thinking skills and were faster at completing memory tests. *Sample: 60 people average age 73. John Hopkins School of Medicine, Baltimore. August 2013.*

SLIMMING

The diet industry is worth £2 billion so no wonder it is always offering us new ways to lose weight. We know the answer is to move more and eat less, but still we look for the holy grail – a magic potion that will let us eat what we like and still have a figure to die for.

Scared Out of Your Weights

Watch a horror film to lose weight. People watching a frightening film like 'The Shining' or 'Jaws' for 90 minutes burn off as many calories as they would in half an hour's walk. The scarier the movie, the more the heart rate soared. *University of Westminster. October 2012.*

But avoid gloomy news programmes on TV – they could make you fat because you could increase your comfort eating by 40 per cent. *University of Miami. January 2013.*

Cheerful TV is just as bad. Some people eat more junk food when they are happy. Contrary to the comfort eating theory, students ate more chocolate and crisps after watching positive TV clips than negative ones. *Sample: 87 students. Maastricht University. May 2013.*

Ladies Who Munch

Middle-aged slimmers who lunch out with friends at least once a week lose on average five pounds less a week than those who eat at home. And those who keep food journals and note everything they eat lose six pounds more than those who don't. *Sample: 123 overweight women aged 50 to 75. Fred Hutchinson Cancer Research Center, Washington. July 2013.*

If you must eat out, lunch with friends who choose low calorie foods. Women at a lunch buffet were significantly influenced by those around them and ate 200 fewer calories if their companions chose the healthy option. *Sample: 100 women. University of Birmingham. September 2012.*

Standing Orders

Standing burns more calories than sitting, so computer desks should be adjusted so that office workers sit less and stand more. Three extra hours on their feet burns 8lbs in a year. *Chester University. January 2013.*

One Step at Time

Forget running up stairs two or three at a time. You may burn more energy initially, but you use up fewer calories by the time you get to the top of five flights than if you go up one by one *University of Roehampton. December 2012.*

Sweet Illusion

So-called 'healthy' soft drinks contain more sugar than you think. People overestimated the amount of sugar in fizzy drinks, but under-estimated it in pure apple juice, a caffeinated energy drink and a smoothie by two to four teaspoons. *Sample: 2,000 adults. Glasgow University. April 2012.*

Not All Sweetness and Light

Artificial sweeteners fail to trigger the feeling of fullness and could lead to over-eating. Some fizzy drinks could even increase the risk of high blood pressure. *Purdue University, Indiana. July 2013.*

The British Dietetic Association disagrees and, you'd never guess, The British Soft Drinks Association does, too.

Size Matters

Large? Eat a big breakfast, including cake, and you will lose more weight. The bigger, sweeter start to the day kick-starts the metabolism and staves off cravings later.   Women eating a big breakfast lost an average of 19lbs over 12 weeks, while those eating most of their calories at the end of the day lost 7.9lbs. *Two studies by Tel Aviv University. February 2012 and August 2013.*

Small? Eat a smaller breakfast to beat the bulge. Overweight people ate one breakfast of 700 calories, one of 560 and one of 230 calories. Those who ate less didn't make up for it later and reduced their daily intake by about 270 calories. *Sample: 30 overweight men and women. Cambridge Medical Research Council. May 2013.*

None at all? Eat no breakfast at all and you are likely to gain weight. Brain scans of people who fasted showed they find sugary foods enticing by late morning and don't eat a nutritious lunch.

Sample: 21 adults. Imperial College, London. October 2012.

A Weight off Your Mind

Overweight women improved their memories after being on a six-months diet. Their brain scans showed they were more efficient at storing memories after they lost weight. *Sample: 20 women, average age 61. Umea University, Sweden. June 2013.*

I must Remember to Diet

Older people who keep to a low-calorie diet are less likely to suffer from mild memory loss than those who overeat. The risk is more than twice as high in people who eat between 2,100 and 6,000 calories a day. *Sample: 1,200 people aged 70 to 89. Mayo Clinic, Arizona. February 2012.*

Destiny Shapes Our Ends

Believing in fate could make you fat. People who think the responsibility for losing weight is out of their hands exercise less, eat the wrong foods and smoke and drink more than those who believe their life is their own responsibility. *Sample: 7,000 adults. Melbourne Institute of Applied Economics and Social Research. September 2012.*

Bone Up on This

Fat people risk thinner bones. Adults with the most fat in their liver and muscles were found to have the highest levels of fat in their bone marrow, which could lead to osteoporosis. *Sample: 106 obese people. Harvard Medical School. July 2013.*

Some Mothers Do 'Ave 'em

Toddlers who have a bad relationship with their mothers are more likely to grow up fat. Those with the worst emotional relationships are two-and-a-half times more likely to be obese by the time they are 15 than those who got along just fine. *Sample: 1,000 toddlers and their mothers. Ohio State University. December 2011.*

Timing is Everything

Eating late in the day means your body stores more fat. So the old saying 'breakfast like a king, lunch like a prince and dine like a pauper' may help to keep you slim. *Sample: Mice. Vanderbilt University, Tennessee. February 2013.*

Crash Diet?

Obese motorists are more at risk in a car crash. Their extra fat stops the seat belt tightening properly and they are 80 per cent more likely to be killed. For women the risk doubles. *Sample: 6,806 motorists, more than 1,000 obese. Emergency Medicine Journal. January 2013.*

Sleep It Off

Sleep longer and your diet will work better. Overweight slimmers who only slept for five and a half hours lost 55 per cent less body fat and 60 per cent more muscle than those who slept for eight and a half hours. *Three studies examined at Eastern Ontario Research Institute. September 2012.*

Lack of sleep makes you snack more. People who slept for five hours a night gained two pounds in weight over seven days as they ate more calories in the form of after-dinner snacks. When they had enough sleep they reduced their intake of fat and carbohydrates.
Sample: 16 young adults. Colorado University. March 2013.

Fast Food Flab

Only three hours after a meal your body can store up to three teaspoons of fat round your midriff. Regular overeating prevents the body drawing on this store to feed muscle. *Oxford University. May 2012.*

Law of Diminishing Returns

The fatter you get the less you remember. Even healthy people, without high blood pressure and high blood sugar, showed a tendency to memory loss over ten years if they were obese. *INSERM medical research institution, France. August 2012.*

Face up to It.

Facebook could make you fat. Chatting on line to friends raises self-confidence and so lowers self-control. Those who used it most were more likely to eat unhealthy snacks and had a higher-than-average ratio of weight to height. They had more credit card debt, too. *Sample: Five studies by Columbia and Pittsburgh Universities. December 2012.*

Belief System

As long as you believe a meal is bigger than it is, you can curb your appetite. People given what appeared to be a small bowl of soup were hungrier two hours later than those who thought they had drunk a large bowl, although the quantity was the same. *Sample: 100 adults. Bristol University. December 2012.*

Weight Watchers

Watching cookery programmes, it appears, encourages us to eat sugary snacks. From a selection of bowls of chocolate-covered sweets, cheese curls and raw carrots, viewers of nature programmes were more likely to choose the carrots, while the cookery addicts got through more chocolates, even when they were watching shows that promoted healthy food. *Sample: 80 adults. Hobart and William Smith Colleges, New York. November 2012.*

A Waist of Time

Counting calories won't make you slimmer, after all. Nutritional advice is based on outdated 19th century science, so counting calories based on food labels won't help you lose weight. The way food is cooked will affect how many calories are absorbed – and so will your metabolism. It's all to do with the amount of certain bacteria in the gut which makes some people more efficient at absorbing calories. *North Carolina State University. August 2013.*

EXERCISE

How much is too much? How little is not enough? The only thing research seems to prove is that any exercise is better than none. If any other conclusions seem at all contradictory – they are.

They Must be Joking

Walkies!

Walk briskly for one hour and fifteen minutes a week and you could extend your life by nearly two years. Double it and you might live seven years longer. *Sample: 600,000 men and women over 40. US government research and Harvard University. November 2012.*

If you step up your walk to an hour and a half every day you could reduce the risk of breast cancer by 33 per cent by preventing the formation of fatty tissue. *Sample: 3,059 women aged 20 to 98. University of North Carolina. June 2012.*

A regular brisk walk can help lower the risk of high blood pressure and high cholesterol, too.
Sample: 33,060 runners and 15,045 walkers over six years.
Lawrence Berkeley National Laboratory, California. April 2013.

Walk, cycle or go by bus to work to cut the risk of diabetes. Of those who drove to work, 19 per cent were obese, compared with 15 per cent of walkers and 13 per cent of cyclists. *Sample: 20,000 adults over two years. Imperial College, London. August 2013.*

They Must be Joking

Hard Slog

Regular jogging for one to two and a half hours a week so that you feel a little, but not very, breathless increases the life expectancy of men by 6.2 years and women by 5.6 years. *Sample: 2,000 men and women joggers and non-joggers. Copenhagen City Heart Study ongoing since 1976.*

Cold Comfort

Exercise too much and you will be more prone to catch a cold. A regular brisk walk can help prevent colds because it strengthens the body's defences against nose and throat infections. But studies of marathon runners show that prolonged strenuous exercise increases the likelihood of becoming ill. *University of Loughborough. January 2012.*

....So keep it short

Two and a half minute bursts of exercise with rests in between are just as good as a hard, time-consuming run. A brisk walk can cut fat in the blood by 11 per cent and hard pedalling on an exercise bike by 33 per cent – the equivalent of a 90-minute run. *Sample: Men aged 18 to 35. Aberdeen University. September 2012.*

Just a Minute

Even one minute's short, sharp burst of exercise a day can help keep the weight down – try walking briskly upstairs or to the shops, or getting off the bus a stop earlier. *Sample: 4,511 adults for seven days. University of Utah. September 2012.*

Twelve minutes of high-intensity exercise a week in three four-minute bursts could help you to stay fit. But be warned – some doctors think intensive exercise could be dangerous for unfit people. *Sample: 24 overweight but healthy men for 10 weeks. Trondheim University. May 2013.*

It's Never Too Late

Even oldies can extend their lives by two years if they go for a regular walk. Surprise, surprise, giving up smoking, drinking moderately and having an active social life helps, too. *Sample: 1,800 over 75s for 18 years. Karolinska Institutet, Stockholm. August 2012.*

Rise and Shine

Do your exercise before breakfast. Men who exercised before breakfast used up 33 per cent more fat than those who walked after eating. But don't expect a big weight loss – an hour's brisk walk every day for ten days will lose about a pound. *Sample: Ten men. Institute of Cardiovascular and Medical Sciences, Glasgow University. October 2012.*

Slow Down a Bit

Too much exercise is bad for you. Intense exercise for more than an hour or two could damage the heart. An easy 5-20 mile jog of six to seven mph a week is better than a hard slog every day. *Sample: 14,000 runners over 30 years. St Luke's Kansas/John Ochsner Institute New Orleans. November 2012.*

Desk Jobs?

Forget the boss's beady eye and take regular strolls round the office if you want to avoid diabetes. Workers who got up and wandered about for just under two minutes every half hour had lower blood sugar than those who walked for half an hour before sitting down to the day's work. *Sample: 70 adults, University of Otago. July 2013.*

A Walk in the Park

The National Trust's most popular walk burns as many calories as playing football. Mind you, it's six miles long. An 'energy map' showed that people who completed the Bath Skyline walk burned an average of 735 calories, which equals 90 minutes of football or two hours of dancing. *Sample: 22 men and women, aged 24 to 69. University of Bath. August 2013.*

A Calculated Risk

Exercise is no use if you treat yourself afterwards. An hour's aerobics burns about 400 calories and you can put that straight back with a slice of cake. Even running a marathon would not burn off a pound of fat, which is the equivalent of 3,500 calories. *American Council on Exercise. July 2013.*

Take It Easy

Twenty minutes of yoga is better for your memory than the same amount of running or jogging. Students who did the comparison improved their reaction times and accuracy after the yoga session. *University of Illinois. June 2013.*

It's a No-Brainer

Exercise four times a week from childhood onwards helps avoid dementia in later life. Men who exercised regularly lost a third less of their brainpower by the age of 50 and women 25 per cent less. *Sample: 9,000 men and women. King's College, London. March 2013.*

Puzzle it Out

Ditch the crossword – go for a walk. Although a lot of research shows that puzzles and card games are good for keeping the brain active, exercising the little grey cells is not as effective as exercising the body because the latter produces a hormone which protects the brain from memory loss.   *University of Nottingham. January 2013.*

A Weight off your Mind

Weightlifting can improve attention and memory even in people who already have the onset of mild dementia. *Sample: 86 women aged 70 to 80. University of British Columbia. April 2012.*

Aerobics will help, too. *Sample: 47 people with mild memory loss over 12 months. National Centre for Geriatrics and Gerontology, Japan. July 2012.*

Shift the Blame

Shift work tends to stop you exercising and raises the likelihood of heart attacks and strokes. Not only does it disrupt your body clock but leads to unhealthy habits like eating junk food and sleeping badly.

Sample: 34 studies of 2,011,935 people. Stroke Prevention & Atherosclerosis Research Centre, Ontario. July 2012.

The Road to Well is Paved with Good Intentions

Since 2008 we have spent £1 billion on exercise equipment, but only one fifth of us ever uses it before it is banished to the spare room. Three-quarters of adults have bought one or more pieces of equipment and the usual outlay is £235. *Sample: 2,000 adults. Nuffield Health. March 2013.*

IT'S A MAD, MAD WORLD

Research projects aren't alone in coming to daft conclusions. Ministerial departments, commercial surveys, local councils and Crown courts all produce unbelievable evidence that we live in a crazy world. As long as we don't take it all too seriously, most of it is good for a laugh.

If You Don't Eat You'll Be Hungry.

Do without breakfast and you will be hungry by 11am. When 21 people were shown pictures of various foods, the ones who had started the day with only a cup of coffee were more tempted by mid-morning sugary snacks than those who had eaten a hearty breakfast. *Imperial College. October 2012.*

Don't Drive if You're Blind

Among the advice issued to mobility scooter users: "If you are eligible to be registered as severely sight impaired (blind), you should not drive a mobility vehicle." *Department of Transport guidelines. March 2012.*

Little Brothers Are a Pain

Having a younger brother can raise a child's blood pressure by six per cent and a younger sister will raise it by four per cent – probably because the older child receives less attention. *Sample: 374 adults. Brandeis University, Massachusetts. November 2012.*

You're Telling Me

Looking vulnerable and acting dumb is the way to attract men. They are genetically programmed to look for easy conquests. Be warned. It doesn't necessarily mean they want a long-term relationship. *Sample: 179 men and 91 women. Texas-Austin University. May 2012.*

What Gave You That Idea?

The more you drink the more attractive you think you are – proved by asking participants to blow into a breathalyser and rate their own attractiveness. *Universiy of Grenoble. July 2012.*

www.clicktillyouresick.com

Nearly a quarter of Brits have shopped on line when drunk and 40 per cent of them later regretted what they bought – including a pair of fake teeth. *Sample: 2,000 on-line shoppers. Survey by Broadband Choices. March 2013.*

Artful Dodgers

Asked about Renoir, 13 per cent of young Brits thought he was a French footballer, six per cent put him down as the French prime minister and one in twenty thought he was last year's Eurovision winner. *Artfinder. April 2013.*

It Doesn't Add Up

One in three British adults would need a calculator to add up to more than 100. When it comes to multiplication, 13 per cent of over 55s and 22 per cent of under 45s struggled with the 11 times table, and a third of 18 to 25-year-olds relied on calculators.

Sample: 2,000 adults. BAE Systems. March 2013.

The Fair Sex

Women are fairer than men and so make better bosses. They consult more and make decisions more likely to benefit everyone, from staff to investors, rather than just the members of the board. *Sample: 600 board members. McMaster University Canada and A. T. Still University, Arizona. March 2013.*

Seeing Red

Men get seduced by red labels. Sales prices written in red convinced men that they were saving nearly twice as much as when the pricing was just in black and white. Women weren't led astray by the colour.

Sample: 400 men and women. Oxford University. March 2013.

The Name's Bondage

People with sexual fetishes are happier, more outgoing and have better mental health than those who never get beyond the missionary position. *Tilburg University, Holland. May 2013.*

Too much information?

Five hundred men and women were asked about their hugging habits. The average cuddle lasted 47 minutes and 36 seconds (most likely while watching TV or a film) but only one in six led to sex. *University of Michigan. October 2012.*

Give Yourself a Boast

Bragging about yourself – in person or on line – makes you feel better. It's as good as food, money or sex because it increases activity in the area of the brain linked to enjoyment. Given the chance, boasters would rather give up money than the chance to gush about themselves. *Harvard University. May 2012.*

Seven-year Hitch

Far from succumbing to the seven-year itch, couples who stay together that long are likely to see their marriages last. After ten years their chance of getting divorced reduces to half what it was on their wedding day. Years four and five are the most likely for separation. *The Marriage Foundation. February 2013.*

Not to be Sniffed At

More than three quarters of us check whether food is fit to eat just by sniffing it. Although food poisoning affects more than 1.7 million people in the UK every year, more than 40 per cent of consumers eat food beyond its sell-by date and one in three would eat food which has dropped on the floor. *Food Standards Agency. June 2013.*

'Allo, 'Allo

Twenty per cent of Britons don't know the meaning of 'bonjour', but 43 per cent can say 'un cerveza por favor' in Spanish. ('a beer please'). More than 64 per cent admit they don't know a single word in any foreign language. *Hotels.com. November 2011.*

What's in a Name?

Dull and Boring are to twin with another town with an exciting name – Bland. Dull is in Scotland and is twinned with Boring in Oregon. Bland Shire is in New South Wales. *Australian Broadcasting Corporation. May 2013.*

Swiss Cheese Plants?

Asked where cheese comes from, one in three primary school children thought it was produced by plants. *Sample: 27,500 children. British Nutrition Foundation. June 2013.*

D-d-d-double W-w-w-whammy

A robber who demanded money from a supermarket where he was a regular customer was recognised because he stuttered. He then tried to escape with £108 but his get-away car got stuck in the snow. *Edinburgh High Court. November 2011.*

Drawing a Little Comfort

Can't resist junk food? All you need is a pencil. Hungry students were asked to draw pictures of pizza, cupcakes, strawberries or peppers. The ones who drew pizzas improved their mood by 28 per cent, cupcakes by 27 per cent and strawberries 22 per cent. Peppers were a no-no at one per cent. *St Bonaventure University, New York. July 2013.*

Text-speak

Looking for evidence to link a thief to a smashed back-door window, police found a message on his phone telling a friend "I've told you 20 times – don't ring me when I'm out robbing." *Leicester Crown Court, December 2012.*

Jammy Dodgers

A traffic census set up at 7.30am to help congestion had to be stopped by 9.30am – because it was causing a traffic jam. *Norfolk County Council. November 2012.*

Mastermind

Mothers answer more questions every hour than are asked at Prime Minister's Question Time. A quarter of children don't ask their fathers because they only say 'ask your Mum'. *Sample: 1,000 mothers with children aged two to ten. Littlewoods on-line survey. March 2013.*

Sweet Nothings

The calories in chocolate are not like 'normal calories': they offset the fat by making your metabolism work faster. People who ate chocolate regularly were found to have a lower BMI than those who didn't, despite consuming the same number of calories and taking no extra exercise. *Sample 972 adults, average age 57. University of California, San Diego. March 2012.*

Lying by the Seat of their Pants

Guilt can be felt just through sitting in a chair. A group of students were told, one by one, that they were in a chair recently occupied by someone who had stolen from the university department. They recorded a greater sense of something being wrong than those who sat in the same chair not knowing that its previous occupant had been a thief. *Sample: Fifty-four students. Loyola University, New Orleans. September 2013.*

Are You Being Served?

A couple of thieves forced a shop assistant into a cubicle and demanded money. They were disturbed by a customer and instead of running away they pretended to work in the shop and sold her a scarf. Not only did they escape detection but she paid them in cash. *Daily Telegraph report. October 2012.*

Moët et Canon

Drop for drop champagne is cheaper than printer ink. Even expensive champagne at £109 a bottle is estimated to cost 15p per millilitre, while the ink (average cost £45 for a set of colour cartridges) comes out at 51p per millilitre. *Which? Computing report. 2012.*

Obvious, Innit?

The less couples argue, the happier they are – and the longer they stay healthy. So don't argue over money and the in-laws and then go storming off to the pub. Stay in and share a healthy meal – you will sleep better and have less stress. *Sample: 1,700 married adults for 20 years. Brigham Young University, Utah. July 2013.*

Britannia Who?

The image of Britannia on the back of the 50p piece is mistaken for Boadicea, Queen Victoria and Mrs Thatcher by one in four British adults who don't recognise the personificaton of Britain, although she has appeared on our coins since 1672. *The Royal Mint. July 2013.*

Cloth Ears?

The children's nursery rhyme 'Baa Baa Black Sheep' was changed to 'Baa Baa Little Sheep' at an Easter concert by a nursery school.   Political correctness? Or perhaps their   teacher had cloth ears and couldn't tell the new version didn't scan.   *Kingston-upon-Thames. April 2012.*

Junk the Broccoli

You may think you are encouraging your man to eat healthily by giving him salad and broccoli, but he only eats them to keep the peace. He will head straight down to the local chippy as soon as he gets the chance to make up for the misery. *Sample: 83 men. University of Michigan. May 2012.*

Value Added Tax

Novel excuses for not taxing the car include 'My dog ate the reminder,' 'I fell out of a tree picking plums,' and 'I couldn't leave the house to buy a new tax disc because I'd taken too much Viagra.' *Driver and Vehicle Licensing Authority. July 2013.*